The Fox and the Hen

By

Nancy J. Nielsen

Illustrated by

Reggie Holladay

Columbus, OH

SRAonline.com

 SRA

Send all inquiries to this address:
SRA/McGraw-Hill
4400 Easton Commons
Columbus, OH 43219

Printed in the United States of America.

ISBN: 978-0-07-611271-5
MHID: 0-07-611271-3

    2 3 4 5 6 7 8 9 MAL 13 12 11 10 09 08

The **McGraw·Hill** Companies

Contents

Chapter 1

Hen

*Hen can sew. She gets her kit. Hen pins a hem. Now she will sew the hem. Next she will sew a sash.

Hen can mend. She will mend a bunch of socks. She will mend socks for Sheep. She will mend socks for Ram. But will she mend a sock for Fox?

Fox is on the hill. Fox looks* down at Hen. He can see her in the morning. He can see her at lunch. Will Fox have Hen for dinner?

Hen is rushing to the well. She drops a pot in the well. She gets water with the pot.

Hen pecks at the corn. She drops the corn in her sack. Then she picks up a stick.

Now Hen is back in her shed. She locks the door.

"Fox is after me," Hen says. "I will not help Fox. I will not let him in my shed."

Chapter 2

Fox

"Boil the water," Fox says to his mom. "We will eat Hen for dinner."

*Now Fox is down the hill. He runs to the shed. He gets in a box by the door.

Hen goes to get corn.

Fox jumps out of the box. He opens the door and runs in. Fox gets under the rug.

Hen runs in. She locks the door. Then Fox jumps up. Hen drops her sack. She flaps up* and lands on the clock.

"You can not get me," Hen tells Fox. "Go back to the den."

Chapter 3

Will Fox Get Hen?

*Can Fox trick Hen? Fox can run round and round. He is quick. He runs faster and faster.

Hen sees Fox running round and round. The running gets to Hen. She feels sick.

Hen is tipping. The tipping sends Hen down.

Hen drops to the rug. "Ouch!" she says.

Fox grabs the sack. He grips Hen by her legs. Fox* flips Hen in to the sack.

Chapter 4

Can Hen Stop Fox?

Fox runs down the path with the sack on his back. The sack is swinging. The sack is tipping.

Hen is in the sack. *Bump! Bump! Bump!* She still feels sick.

"How lucky I am!" Fox says. "I will go to my den where the fire is hot."

*"Think!" Hen says. "What will I do? How can I get help now?"

Then Fox stops.

"My legs feel sore," Fox says. "I can not run fast with this sack. I will stop and rest."

Hen thinks and thinks. She thinks of her kit. It is in her sash. Hen grabs her kit.

Hen is slick and quick. She cuts* the sack. *Clip! Clip! Clip!*

Hen slips out of the sack. She picks up a rock and slips it in the sack. Hen sews the sack up. Fox is still sleeping.

Zzz

17

Hen runs back to her shed. She slips in the door. She locks the door.

"Fox can not eat me for dinner now," Hen says.

Chapter 5

Dinner

Fox gets up. He grabs the sack. He runs to his den.

"I set a pot of water on the fire to boil," Mom Fox says. "Have you got Hen?"

"Yes, I got her. Dinner will be sweet," Fox says to his mom. "You lift the lid. I will drop her in."

*Mom Fox steps up to the pot and opens the lid. She has a fork in her hand. Fox steps up to the pot. He opens the sack. He tips the sack.

Ding! The rock slams in to the pot. Hot water is rushing up. The hot pot boils over. Hot water runs down the pot. It gets on Fox* and his mom.

"Ouch! Ouch! This water is hot!" Fox and his mom yell. They hop up and down. Fox rubs his hand.

Fox goes to the creek and gets a tub of cold water. Fox and his mom hop in the tub. But they still feel bad.

"Where is my sweet dinner? Where is that Hen?" Mom Fox says. "Did she trick you again?"

"She did trick me," Fox says. He feels sick. "I will not try to get Hen for dinner again."

Fox and his mom did not get dinner. They went to bed.

Chapter 6

Hen Again

Hen is pinning a hem. Sheep and Ram tap at her door. Hen peeks out. She lets them in.

"Will you mend this sock?" Sheep asks.

*"Yes, I will fix it for you," Hen says. She looks up the hill, but she can not see Fox or his mom.

"Fox and his mom feel sick," Sheep says. "They set a pot to boil. The hot water got on them."

"You will not see Fox again," Ram says.

Hen grins. She cracks corn. She drops the corn* in a pot. Hen boils a pot of corn for Ram and Sheep.